Contents

Size of short letters

These letters are short letters. They are all the same size. The short letter line shows the height of these letters.

Most short letters start at the short letter line. The letter **e** starts lower but it curves up to the short letter line.

r n m i u v w x z c o a s e

1   Trace each short letter. Then write two of your own. Keep all your letters the same size.

r   n   m

c   o   a

i   u   x

v   z   w

2   Trace and continue the pattern.

eses eses

Copy each word twice.

rim   ice

wax   use

zoo   van

Apply it

Write the letters **s** or **es** to complete each caption. Then copy the captions.

six ice cream cone

seven new coin

nine cross

some runner   in a race

Size of tall letters

These letters are tall letters. They have a tall stick. Tall letters are nearly twice the size of short letters. The tall letter line shows the height of most tall letters.

The letter **t** is not quite as tall. It starts just below the tall letter line.

l h b k f d t

1 Trace each tall letter. Then write two of your own.

2 Trace and continue the patterns.

Practise it

Copy each word twice.

hid   full

fat   kit

bed   tub

Apply it

Copy the caption for each picture.

the little kitten

_____

the fluffy blanket

_____

the thickest book

_____

the tallest ladder

_____

Size of letters with tails

These letters have a body and a tail. The body is the same size as a short letter. The tail is nearly the same length as the body.

To write these letters, always start at the short letter line. The tails go down to the tail letter line. Keep all the tails the same length.

g   q   j   y   p

1   Trace each letter. Then write two of your own. Keep the body and the tail of your letters about the same size.

g g   q q

j j   y y

p p   p p

2   Trace and continue the patterns.

qgqg qgqg

yjyj yjyj

Copy each word twice.

pig   joy

jug   quiz

pay   gap

Apply it

Copy the caption for each picture.

my happy puppy

the big digger

my toy yoyo

a jolly juggler

Size of capital letters

All capital letters are the same size. The tall letter line shows the height of capital letters.

To write capital letters, start at the tall letter line or just below it.

A B C D E F G

1 Trace and copy each capital letter. Keep all your letters the same size.

2 Trace and continue the pattern.

Copy each word in capital letters.

SLOW   MENU

EXIT   WAIT

OPEN   SALE

Apply it

Write each classroom sign using capital letters.

our book corner

OUR BOOK CORNER

wash your hands

please tidy up

the quiet area

Capital and lowercase letters

Capital letters are nearly twice the height of most lowercase letters. They are the same height as tall letters.

Some capital letters and lowercase letters are the same shape, but the capital letter is nearly twice the size.

Ii Kk Ll Mm Nn Oo

Try it

1 Trace each lowercase letter. Then write it as a capital letter.

2 Trace and continue the patterns.

Copy each name.

Alfie

Scott

Mark

Abdul

Nisha

Helen

Write the capital letter to complete each day of the week. Then copy the days in the correct order.

Monday

ednesday

uesday

unday

aturday

riday

hursday

Monday

Size of numbers

All numbers are the same size. They are the same height as tall letters and capital letters. The tall letter line shows the height of numbers.

To write numbers, start at the tall letter line or just below it.

0 1 2 3 4 5 6 7 8 9

1 Trace each number. Then write two of your own. Keep all your numbers the same size.

2 Trace and continue the patterns.

Practise it

Copy each postcode.

SG19 3RA

NK60 2SY

BD78 5HP

Apply it

Write the number to complete each date. Then copy the dates.

Wednesday ____ th March

Tuesday ____ th August

20th July

5th November

Position of short letters

All short letters sit on the baseline. They go down to touch the line. They do not float above the line or sink below it.

a c e i m n o r s u v w x z

1 Copy each letter twice. Keep all your letters on the line.

r   m   i

c   o   a

u   s   e

w   x   z

2 Trace and continue the patterns.

Copy each word.

never   mixer

comic   craze

swim   nurse

Apply it

Write the word **was** or **saw** to complete each sentence. Then copy the sentences.

The cow _____ near a river.

Erin _____ on a seesaw.

We _____ a man in a car.

Gran _____ a mouse.

Position of tall letters

The tall letters **h**, **b**, **k**, **l**, **t** and **d** all sit on the baseline. They go down to touch the line. The letter **f** is a tall letter, but it also has a tail.

h   b   k   l   t   d   f

Try it

1   Copy each letter twice. Keep all your letters on the line.

h   b   k

l   t   d

2   Trace and continue the patterns.

hkhk   hkhk

adad   adad

llbll   llbll

ilt   ilt

Copy each word.

hutch   blink

think   told

black   third

Write the letters **ed** to complete each sentence. Then copy the sentences.

A kite land _____ on the hill.

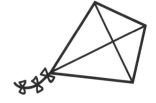

_____

All the butter melt _____.

_____

Dad drill _____ a hole.

_____

I kick _____ the ball back.

_____

Position of letters with tails

These letters have a body and a tail. The body of the letter sits on the baseline like the short letters. The tail hangs below the baseline.

Try it

1 Copy each letter twice. Keep all your letters on the line.

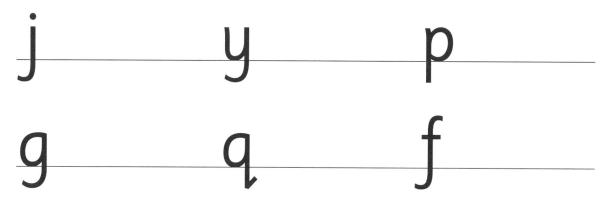

2 Trace and continue the patterns.

Copy each word.

page   jeep

enjoy   yelp

grape   flip

Apply it

Write the letters **ing** to complete each sentence. Then copy the sentences.

The frog is jump_____.

_____

They are play_____.

_____

My dog is yapp_____.

_____

The jet plane is fly_____.

_____

Position of capital letters

All capital letters sit on the baseline. They all start at the tall letter line, or just below it, and go down to touch the baseline.

Q R S T U V W

1 Copy the alphabet in capital letters. Keep all your letters on the line.

ABCDEFGHIJKLM

NOPQRSTUVWXYZ

2 Trace and continue the patterns.

Write each word in capital letters.

vets   VETS   farm

zoo   park

shop   cafe

Write a word in capital letters to complete each sentence. Then copy the sentences.

FEE FI FO FUM   !

_____

TRIP TRAP TRIP   !

_____

They PULLED and   .

_____

He BLEW and   .

_____

Position of capital and lowercase letters

All capital letters sit on the baseline. Most lowercase letters sit on the baseline. These lowercase letters have tails that hang below the baseline.

Gg Qq Jj Yy Pp Ff

Try it

1   Copy each capital and lowercase letter twice. Keep all your letters on the line.

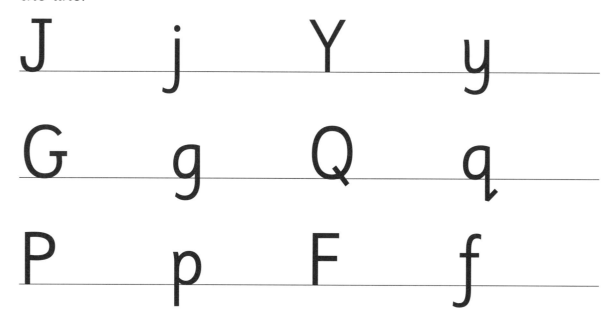

J   j   Y   y

G   g   Q   q

P   p   F   f

2   Trace and continue the patterns.

YyYy YyYy

PpPp PpPp

Copy each name. Make sure you start each name with a capital letter.

poppy   yusuf

vijay   freya

greg   jenny

Apply it

Copy each sentence. Write capital letters at the start of any names.

I fly to paris on friday.

peggy was born in july.

geeta lives in york.

jess goes to gorway school.

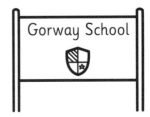

Position of numbers

All numbers sit on the baseline. They all start at the tall letter line, or just below it, and go down to touch the baseline.

0 1 2 3 4 5 6 7 8 9

1 Copy each number. Keep all your numbers on the line.

11   12   13

14   15   16

17   18   19

2 Trace and continue the patterns.

Copy each price twice.

20p   45p

16p   25p

38p   49p

Apply it

Copy the name and address from each envelope.

Mr Jake Brown

23 Park Street

Weston

WS6 5GP

Mrs Ashton

47 Green Lane

Redwell

RD8 9EY

Spacing within words

The letters within a word sit close together, but they do not touch.

There should be no large gaps between the letters in a word or between parts of the word.

letters ✓   letters ✗   letters ✗

Try it

1   Tick the three words that show correct spacing.

ove r ☐   qu ick ☐   here ☐

A pril ☐   went ☐   your ☐

ve ry ☐   a way ☐   Sasha ☐

2   Trace and copy each word. Make sure you use correct spacing.

over   here

your   quick

went   April

Copy each word.

under   today

begin   again

after   every

Apply it

Write a word to complete each sentence. Then copy the sentences.

farmyard   birthday   sheepdog

I went to a farm on my _____.

_____

I saw hens in the _____.

_____

I met Jess the _____.

_____

Spacing between words

Spaces are left between words in a sentence so that it is easier to read.

The spaces between words should all be the same size. They should be about the size of the letter **o**.

<u>Leave</u> <u>spaces</u> <u>between</u> <u>words</u>.

Try it

1 Tick the sentence that shows correct spacing.

<u>I am happy</u>. ☐

<u>It wasreally fun</u>. ☐

<u>Weplayedagame</u>. ☐

2 Copy each sentence. Make sure you leave spaces between words.

<u>I had a bad cold</u>.

<u>I felt very sad</u>.

Schofield & Sims **WriteWell**

Copy the sentence, leaving spaces between the words.

I sat on the garden gate and I saw a red van.

_____

_____

Complete each sentence with your own words.

I went to the zoo and _____

_____

It was raining and _____

_____

I saw a monkey and _____

_____

Then we _____

_____

Punctuation focus

Full stops, exclamation marks and question marks are used to complete sentences. The dot always sits on the baseline straight after the last word.

Exclamation marks and question marks are the same height as tall letters and capital letters.

How do you feel?   I feel great!

Try it

1   Copy each punctuation mark 10 times. Keep all your punctuation marks the same size.

!

?

2   Trace and continue the patterns. Make sure your dot always sits on the line.

Copy each word and the punctuation mark.

When?   How?

Boom!   Thud!

What?   Crash!

Write a question mark or exclamation mark to complete each sentence.
Then copy the sentences.

The monster is coming

_____

Where can we hide

_____

What shall we do

_____

Run away

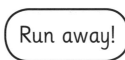

Run away!

_____

WriteWell challenge 1

Copy this rhyme in your best writing. Then draw pictures and patterns to go with your rhyme.

Raindrops

Pitter patter falls the rain

_____

On the roof and window pane.

_____

Softly softly it comes down.

_____

It makes a stream that runs around.

_____

Schofield & Sims **WriteWell**

WriteWell challenge 2

Write a party invitation. Use your best writing. Decorate the invitation.

Dear _____

You are invited to _____

Date _____

Time _____

At _____

Please come and _____

_____

We will eat _____

Please call _____ to let

me know if you can come.

From _____

Book Five
Letter Size and Position

Schofield & Sims WriteWell is a complete course designed to guide children from their first steps in mark-making towards the development of secure, fluent and comfortable joined handwriting that can be adapted for a range of purposes.

Handwriting is a complex process that requires the simultaneous use of cognitive, physical and perceptual skills. As development can vary greatly from child to child, **Schofield & Sims WriteWell** splits learning into manageable modules, offering you the flexibility to select the appropriate book for your child's needs. Young writers can then move through the programme at their own pace as their handwriting skills flourish – a highly personalised approach that ensures a confident foundation for every child.

This is WriteWell 5: Letter Size and Position. **In this book, handwriting lines are used to teach relative letter size. Children also learn to position and space writing on the baseline. This book includes 15 teaching units, each containing activities that gradually increase in difficulty, and two summative WriteWell Challenge tasks, designed to showcase new learning and encourage children to take pride in their handwriting skills.**

Stage 1
Shape

Stage 2
Space, size and sitting on the line

Stage 3
Stringing together and slant

Stage 4
Speed and style

Published by Schofield & Sims Ltd,
7 Mariner Court, Wakefield, West Yorkshire WF4 3FL, UK

This edition copyright © Schofield & Sims Ltd, 2019. First published in 2019. Second impression 2020

Author: Carol Matchett. Carol Matchett has asserted her moral rights under the Copyright, Designs and Patents Act, 1988, to be identified as the author of this work.

British Library Cataloguing in Publication Data
A catalogue record for this book is available from the British Library.

Design by Oxford Designers & Illustrators Ltd. Cover design by Ledgard Jepson Ltd
Printed in the UK by Page Bros (Norwich) Ltd

Schofield&Sims

For further information and to place your order visit www.schofieldandsims.co.uk or telephone 01484 607080

MIX
Paper from responsible sources
FSC® C023114

ISBN 978 07217 1637 4
£3.95 (Retail price)

ISBN 978-07217-1637-4

9 780721 716374